Poems about

Colours

Selected by
Amanda Earl & Danielle Sensier

Illustrated by
Frances Lloyd

Wayland

Titles in the series
Poems about . . .

Animals	**Food**
Colours	**Growth**
Day & Night	**Homes**
Families	**Journeys**
Feelings	**Weather**

For the Sandown Playgroup

Series editor: Catherine Baxter
Designer: Loraine Hayes

First published in 1994 by
Wayland (Publishers) Ltd
61 Western Road, Hove
East Sussex BN3 1JD, England

© Copyright 1994 Wayland
(Publishers) Ltd

Typeset by Dorchester Typesetting
Group Ltd, Dorset, England.
Printed and bound in Italy by
G. Canale & C.S.p.A, Turin.

British Library Cataloguing in Publication Data

Poems About Colours. – (Poems About . . .
Series)
I. Earl, Amanda II. Sensier, Danielle
III. Series
808.81936

ISBN 0-7502-1038-9

Front cover design: S. Balley

Poets' nationalities

John Agard	British/Guyanese
Mary Ann Hoberman	American
Dennis Lee	Canadian
A. A. Milne	English
Jack Prelutsky	American
Marchette Chute	Canadian
Marie Louise Allen	American
May Swenson	American
Christina Rossetti	English/Italian

Contents

What is the sun?

The sun is an orange dinghy
    sailing across a calm sea.

It is a gold coin
    dropped down a drain in Heaven.

It is a yellow beach ball
    kicked high into the summer sky.

It is a red thumb-print
   on a sheet of pale blue paper.

It is a milk bottle's gold top
   floating in a puddle.

Wes Magee

A Little Yellow Cricket

A little yellow cricket
At the roots of the corn
Is hopping about and singing.

Papago Tribe

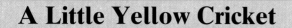

Haiku

Little frog among
rain-shaken leaves, are you, too,
splashed with fresh, green paint?

Gaki

New Shoes

Buying new shoes
takes so long.
When the colour is right
the size is wrong.

The lady asks
How does it fit?
I say to Mum
Pinches a bit.

But that's not true
It's just because
I don't want the brown
I prefer the blue.

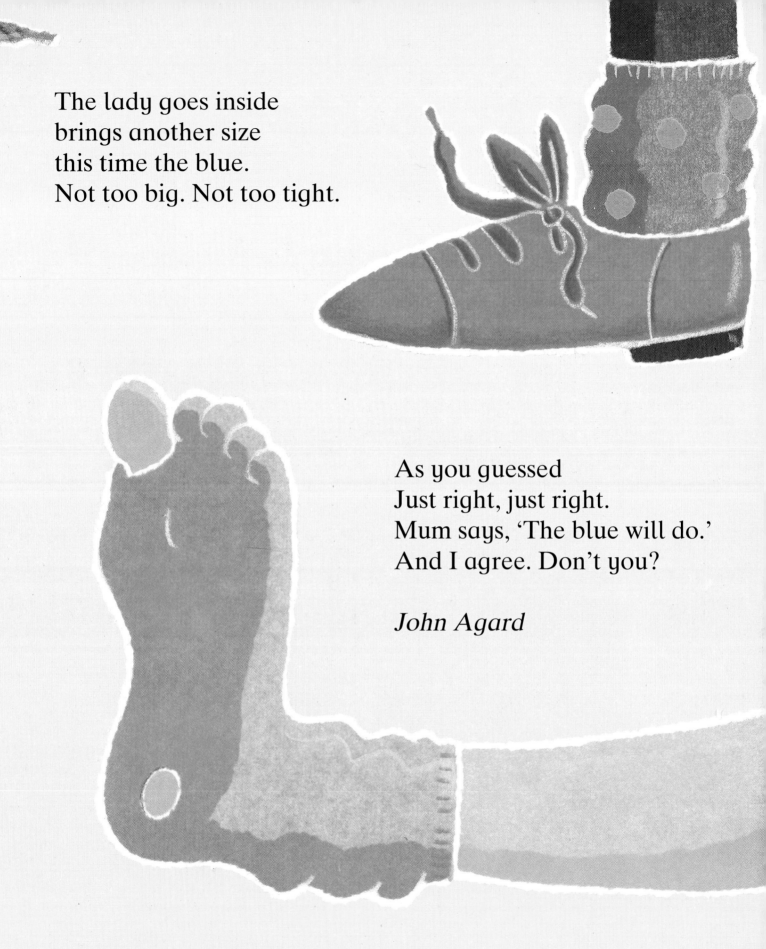

The lady goes inside
brings another size
this time the blue.
Not too big. Not too tight.

As you guessed
Just right, just right.
Mum says, 'The blue will do.'
And I agree. Don't you?

John Agard

9

Foxes

A litter of little black foxes. And later
A litter of little grey foxes. And later
A litter of little white foxes.
The white ones are lighter than grey.
Not a lot.
The grey ones are lighter than black.
Just a little.
The litters are lighter in moonlight.
They glitter
They gleam in the moonlight. They glow and they glisten.
Out on the snow see the silver fox sparkle.

Mary Ann Hoberman

Silverly

Silverly,
   Silverly,
Over the
   Trees
The moon drifts
   By on a
Runaway
   Breeze.

Dozily,
   Dozily,
Deep in her
   Bed,
A little girl
   Dreams with the
Moon in her
   Head.

Dennis Lee

Daffadowndilly

She wore her yellow sun-bonnet,
    She wore her greenest gown;
She turned to the south wind
    And curtsied up and down.
She turned to the sunlight
    And shook her yellow head,
And whispered to her neighbour:
    'Winter is dead.'

A. A. Milne

He's got a shining coat.
It is as yellow as the sun.
When he looks at you he gleams.
And in the night he stays awake
to see what goes by.
Sometimes he sees other daffodils
glow but mostly he sees the moon.

Jo Ellen Turner
(child poet)

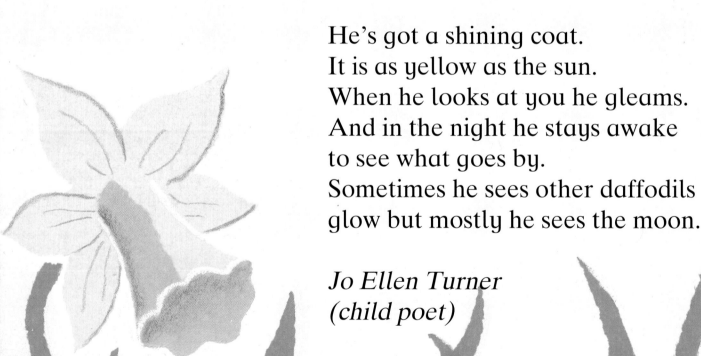

12

My Sister Ate an Orange

My sister ate an orange,
I'm astonished that she did,
she swallowed it completely,
she's a disconcerting kid.

My sister ate an orange,
first she chewed it for awhile,
then digested it entirely
with a silly sort of smile.

My sister ate an orange,
it's a novel thing to do,
then she also ate a yellow
and a purple and a blue.

Jack Prelutsky

Crayons

I've coloured a picture with crayons.
   I'm not very pleased with the sun.
I'd like it much stronger and brighter
   And more like the actual one.
I've tried with the crayon that's yellow,
   I've tried with the crayon that's red.
But none of it looks like the sunlight
   I carry around in my head.

Marchette Chute

16

First Snow

Snow makes whiteness where it falls.
The bushes look like popcorn balls.
And places where I always play,
Look like somewhere else today.

Marie Louise Allen

19

On Early Morning

Peach blossom after rain
Is deeper red;
The willow fresher green;
Twittering overhead;
And fallen petals lie wind-blown,
Unswept upon the courtyard stone.

Early Chinese

I'm glad the sky is painted blue

I'm glad the sky is painted blue,
    And the earth is painted green,
With such a lot of nice fresh air
    All sandwiched in between.

Anonymous

The Zebra

The zebra's neither black nor white
    But has acquired the knack
Of being black AND being white
    Or is it white and black?

Hiawyn Oram

Painting the Gate

I painted the mailbox. That was fun.
I painted it blue.
Then I painted the gate.
I painted a spider that got on the gate.
I painted his mate.
I painted the ivy around the gate.
Some stones I painted blue,
and part of the cat as he rubbed by.
I painted my hair. I painted my shoe.
I painted the slats, both front and back,
all their bevelled edges too.

I painted the numbers on the gate –
I shouldn't have, but it was too late.
I painted the posts, each side and top,
I painted the hinges, the handle, the lock,
several ants and a moth asleep in a crack.
At last I was through.

I'd painted the gate
shut, me out, with both hands dark blue,
as well as my nose, which,
early on, because of a sudden itch,
got painted. But wait!
I had painted the gate.

May Swenson

25

Near the Window Tree

It is grey out.
It is grey in.
In me
It is grey as the day is grey.

The trees look sad
And I,
Not knowing why I do,
Cry.

Karla Kushkin

Dapple-Grey

I took my horse to market
And lost her on the way
For dappled were the moors with rain
And she was dapple-grey.

Hiawyn Oram

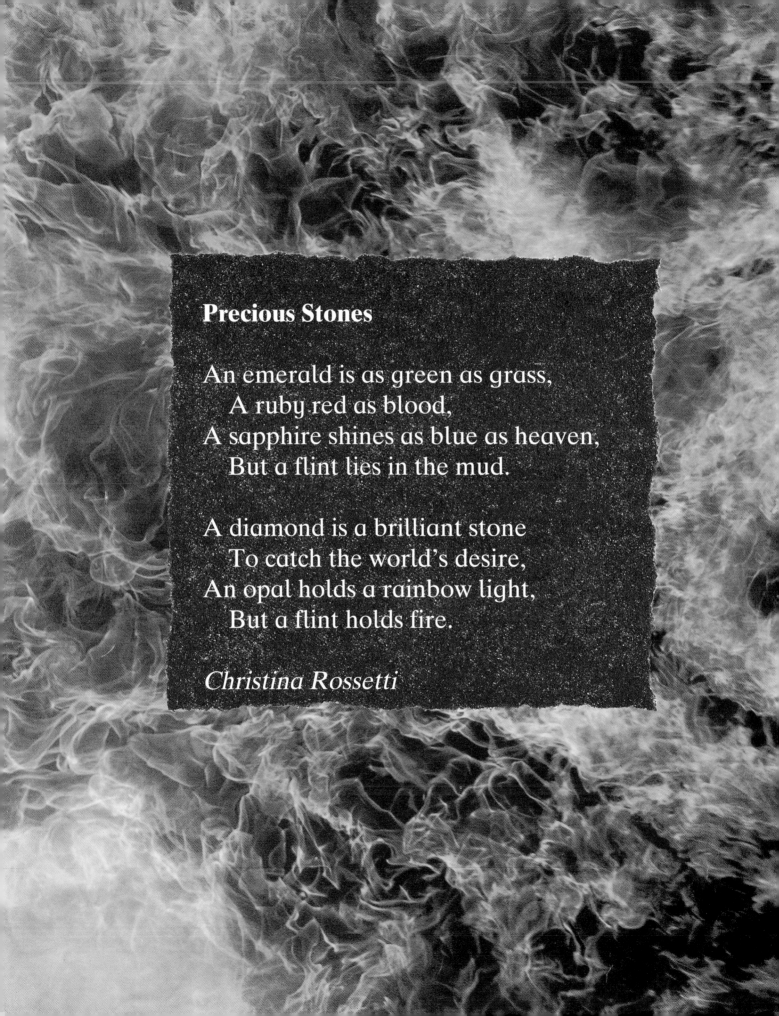

Precious Stones

An emerald is as green as grass,
   A ruby red as blood,
A sapphire shines as blue as heaven,
   But a flint lies in the mud.

A diamond is a brilliant stone
   To catch the world's desire,
An opal holds a rainbow light,
   But a flint holds fire.

Christina Rossetti

What Is Orange?

Orange is a tiger lily,
A carrot,
A feather from
A parrot,
A flame,
The wildest colour
You can name
Orange is a happy day
Saying good-by
In a sunset that
Shocks the sky.

Mary O'Neill

How to use this book

Poetry is a very enjoyable area of literature and children
take to it naturally, usually beginning with nursery rhymes.
It's what happens next that can make all the difference!
This series of thematic poetry anthologies keeps poetry
alive and enjoyable for young children.

When using these books there are several ways in which
you can help a child to appreciate poetry and to understand the
ways in which words can be carefully chosen and sculpted
to convey different atmospheres and meanings. Try to
encourage the following:

- Joining in when the poem is read out loud.
- Talking about favourite words, phrases or images.
- Discussing the illustration and photographs.
- Miming facial expressions to suit the mood of the poems.
- Acting out events in the poems.
- Copying out the words.
- Learning favourite poems by heart.
- Discussing the difference between a poem and a story
- Clapping hands to rhythmic poems
- Talking about metaphors/similes eg what kind of weather
  would a lion be? What colour would sadness be? What
  would it taste like? If you could hold it, how would it
  feel?

It is inevitable that, at some point, children will want to
write poems themselves. Writing a poem is, however, only
one way of enjoying poetry. With the above activities,
children can be encouraged to appreciate and delight in
this unique form of communication.

Picture acknowledgements

Ace 11 (Edmund Nagele); Cephas 26/27 (Alain Proust); Chapel
Studios cover; Impact 13 (Alexis Wallerstein); Life File 14 (Nicola
Sutton), 18 (Jon Woodhouse), 21 (Nicola Sutton); Tony Stone
Worldwide 4/5 (Ian Murphy), 17 (Terry Vine), 28 (Lester Lefkowitz);
Zefa 7 (Flury), 22 (Minden).

Text acknowledgements

For permission to reprint copyright material the publishers gratefully
acknowledge the following: John Agard c/o Caroline Sheldon
Literary Agency for 'New Shoes' from *I Din Do Nuttin* published by
The Bodley Head. Reprinted by permission of the author; Andersen
Press for 'The Zebra' and 'Dapple Grey' from *Out of the Blue* by
Hiawyn Oram and illustrated by David McKee. Reprinted by permission of the publisher; Constable & Company Ltd for 'On Early
Morning' translated by Helen Waddell from *Lyrics from the Chinese*.
Reprinted by permission of the publisher; Gina Maccoby Literary
Agency for 'Foxes' from *The Raucous Auk* by Mary Ann Hoberman
published by Viking Press. Copyright © 1973 by Mary Ann
Hoberman. Reprinted by permission of Gina Maccoby Literary
Agency; Wes Magee for 'What Is The Sun?' by Wes Magee.
Reprinted by permission of the author; Reed Book Services for 'What
is Orange?' from *Hailstones and Halibut Bones* by Mary O'Neil published by William Heinemann. 'Daffadowndilly' from *When We
Were Very Young* by A. A. Milne published by Methuen Children's
Books. Reprinted by permission of Reed Book Services; Elizabeth
Roach for 'Crayons' from *Rhymes About Us* by Marchette Chute
published 1974 by E. P. Dutton. Copyright © 1974 Marchette Chute.
Reprinted by permission of Elizabeth Roach; Jo Turner for 'He's Got
a Shining Coat'. Reprinted by permission of the author. While every
effort has been made to secure permission, in some cases it has proved
impossible to trace the copyright holders. The publishers apologise
for this apparent negligence.

Index of first lines